The 12 Week Journal
for *memorizing*
BIBLE VERSES

More information at: www.123journalit.com

First Printing: January 2017
1 2 3 Journal It Publishing

ISBN-13: 978-0-9986183-0-2

TABLE OF CONTENTS:

This Journal Belongs To:

_ _ _ _ _ _ _ _ _ _ _ _ _ _ _ _

How to use this JOURNAL

1) Choose 12 BIBLE verses.

2) Focus on 1 per WEEK.

3) WRITE it, doodle it, SAY it, ponder it, & PRAY it, until YOU know it, word for WORD.

Brainstorm VERSE ideas . . .

- use your FAVORITES
- choose by TOPIC
- focus on the NEW Testament or the Old TESTAMENT
- get all of them from one BOOK

. . . or try some of these GEMS to get you started:

Romans 8:28	Deuteronomy 6:4	Hebrews 11:1
Ephesians 6:12	Hosea 4:6	James 1:19
Philippians 4:6	Jeremiah 29:11	John 3:16

List 12 VERSES:

1) _____

2) _____

3) _____

4) _____

5) _____

6) _____

7) _____

8) _____

9) _____

10) _____

11) _____

12) _____

. . . ready, set, GO

My VERSE this week:

DATE:

_____

_____

_____

_____

_____

_____

_____

_____

- - - - - - - - - -

What it MEANS to me . . . .

_____

_____

_____

_____

_____

_____

_____

_____

_____

_____

_____

Write the VERSE . . .

_____

_____

_____

_____

_____

_____

_____

and WRITE it again . . .

_____

_____

_____

_____

_____

_____

_____

Say it OUT loud

- ○ DAY #1
- ○ DAY #2
- ○ DAY #3
- ○ DAY #4
- ○ DAY #5
- ○ DAY #6

Draw & doodle it . . . .

Write the VERSE . . .

_____

_____

_____

_____

_____

_____

_____

and WRITE it again . . .

_____

_____

_____

_____

_____

_____

_____

_____

Reflect & turn it into a PRAYER . . .

_____
_____
_____
_____
_____
_____
_____
_____
_____
_____

Now SAY the verse out loud.
& READ the prayer out loud.

Write the VERSE . . . .

_____
_____
_____
_____
_____
_____
_____
_____

and WRITE it again . . . .

_____
_____
_____
_____
_____
_____
_____
_____

Pick 3 KEYWORDS
to spell & define below:

1) _____

_____

_____

_____

2) _____

_____

_____

_____

3) _____

_____

_____

_____

Now whisper each keyword while saying the verse. Repeat 3-5 times.

Write the VERSE . . . .

_____
_____
_____
_____
_____
_____
_____

and WRITE it again . . . .

_____
_____
_____
_____
_____
_____
_____

Go tell SOMEONE

WHO can I tell this week?

_____

WHEN & WHERE will it happen?

_____

WHAT do I want to say?

_____

_____

WHY do I want to tell them?

_____

_____

HOW did THE PERSON receive it?

_____

_____

WHO else can I share this VERSE with?

_____

Spread the GOOD NEWS everyday . . .

Write the VERSE . . . .

_____
_____
_____
_____
_____
_____
_____

and WRITE it again . . .

_____
_____
_____
_____
_____
_____
_____
_____

Last chance to PONDER

. . . write, doodle, draw . . .

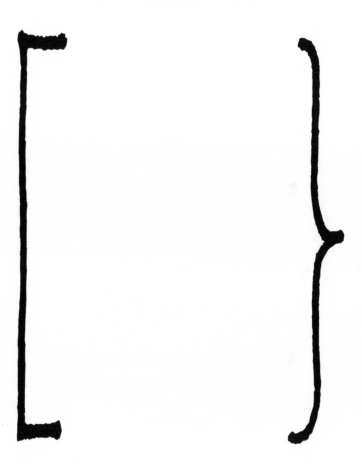

Now CLOSE the journal.
& QUIZ yourself . . .
no peeking!

extra NOTES

My VERSE this week:

DATE: _____

_____
_____
_____
_____
_____
_____
_____
_____

- - - - - - - - - - - - - -

What it MEANS to me . . . .

_____
_____
_____
_____
_____
_____
_____
_____
_____
_____

Write the VERSE . . . .

_____
_____
_____
_____
_____
_____
_____

and WRITE it again . . . .

_____
_____
_____
_____
_____
_____
_____

Say it OUT loud

- DAY #1
- DAY #2
- DAY #3
- DAY #4
- DAY #5
- DAY #6

Draw & doodle it . . .

Write the VERSE . . . .

_____
_____
_____
_____
_____
_____
_____

and WRITE it again . . . .

_____
_____
_____
_____
_____
_____
_____

Reflect & turn it into a PRAYER . . .

_____

_____

_____

_____

_____

_____

_____

_____

_____

_____

Now SAY the verse out loud.
& READ the prayer out loud.

Write the VERSE . . . .

_____

_____

_____

_____

_____

_____

and WRITE it again . . . .

_____

_____

_____

_____

_____

_____

_____

Pick 3 KEYWORDS
to spell & define below:

1) _____

_____

_____

_____

2) _____

_____

_____

_____

3) _____

_____

_____

_____

Now whisper each keyword while saying the verse. Repeat 3-5 times.

Write the VERSE . . .

_____

_____

_____

_____

_____

_____

_____

and WRITE it again . . .

_____

_____

_____

_____

_____

_____

_____

_____

Go tell SOMEONE

WHO can I tell this week?

_____

WHEN & WHERE will it happen?

_____

WHAT do I want to say?

_____
_____
_____

WHY do I want to tell them?

_____
_____
_____

HOW did THE PERSON receive it?

_____
_____
_____

WHO else can I share this VERSE with?

_____

Spread the GOOD NEWS everyday . . .

Write the VERSE . . . .

_____
_____
_____
_____
_____
_____
_____

and WRITE it again . . . .

_____
_____
_____
_____
_____
_____
_____
_____

Last chance to PONDER

. . . write, doodle, draw . . .

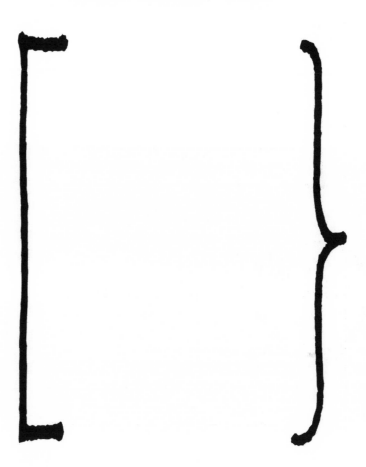

Now **CLOSE** the journal.
& **QUIZ** yourself . . .
no peeking!

extra NOTES

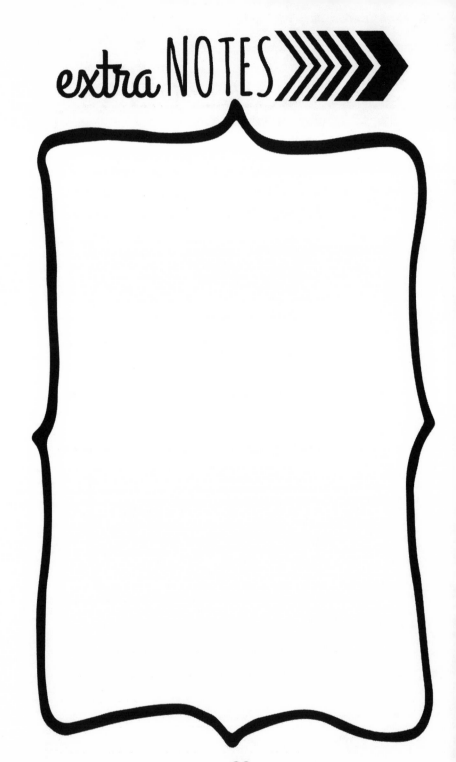

My VERSE this week:

DATE:

_____
_____
_____
_____
_____
_____
_____
_____

- - - - - - - - - - - -

What it MEANS to me . . . .

_____
_____
_____
_____
_____
_____
_____
_____
_____
_____
_____

Write the VERSE . . . .

_____

_____

_____

_____

_____

_____

_____

and WRITE it again . . . .

_____

_____

_____

_____

_____

_____

_____

_____

Say it OUT loud

- ◯ DAY #1
- ◯ DAY #2
- ◯ DAY #3
- ◯ DAY #4
- ◯ DAY #5
- ◯ DAY #6

Draw & doodle it . . . .

Write the VERSE . . . .

_____
_____
_____
_____
_____
_____
_____

and WRITE it again . . . .

_____
_____
_____
_____
_____
_____
_____

Reflect & turn it into a PRAYER . . .

Now SAY the verse out loud.
& READ the prayer out loud.

Write the VERSE . . . .

and WRITE it again . . . .

Pick 3 KEYWORDS
to spell & define below:

1) _____

_____

_____

_____

2) _____

_____

_____

_____

3) _____

_____

_____

_____

Now whisper each keyword while saying the verse. Repeat 3-5 times.

Write the VERSE . . . .

_____
_____
_____
_____
_____
_____
_____

and WRITE it again . . . .

_____
_____
_____
_____
_____
_____
_____
_____

(Go tell) SOMEONE

WHO can I tell this week?

_____

WHEN & WHERE will it happen?

_____

WHAT do I want to say?

_____

_____

WHY do I want to tell them?

_____

_____

HOW did THE PERSON receive it?

_____

_____

WHO else can I share this VERSE with?

_____

Spread the GOOD NEWS everyday . . .

Write the VERSE . . . .

_____

_____

_____

_____

_____

_____

_____

and WRITE it again . . . .

_____

_____

_____

_____

_____

_____

_____

Last chance to PONDER

. . . write, doodle, draw . . .

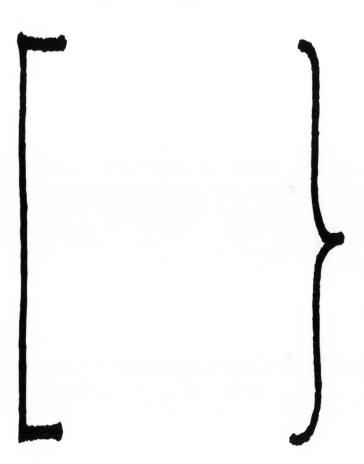

Now **CLOSE** the journal.
& **QUIZ** yourself . . .
no peeking!

extra NOTES >>>>>

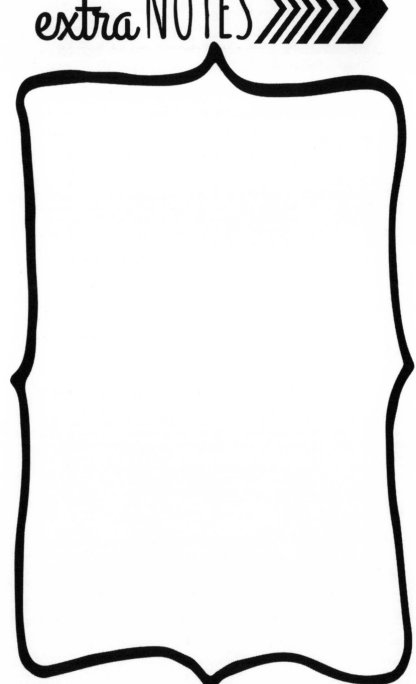

My VERSE this week:

DATE:

_____
_____
_____
_____
_____
_____
_____
_____
_____

- - - - - - - - - - - -

What it MEANS to me . . . .

_____
_____
_____
_____
_____
_____
_____
_____
_____
_____
_____

Write the VERSE . . . .

_____

_____

_____

_____

_____

_____

_____

and WRITE it again . . . .

_____

_____

_____

_____

_____

_____

_____

_____

Say it OUT loud

○ DAY #1
○ DAY #2
○ DAY #3
○ DAY #4
○ DAY #5
○ DAY #6

Draw & doodle it . . . .

Write the VERSE . . . .

_____
_____
_____
_____
_____
_____
_____

and WRITE it again . . . .

_____
_____
_____
_____
_____
_____
_____

Reflect & turn it into a PRAYER . . .

Now **SAY** the verse out loud.
& **READ** the prayer out loud.

Write the VERSE . . . .

_____

_____

_____

_____

_____

_____

_____

and WRITE it again . . . .

_____

_____

_____

_____

_____

_____

_____

Pick 3 KEYWORDS
to spell & define below:

1) _____

_____

_____

_____

2) _____

_____

_____

_____

3) _____

_____

_____

_____

Now whisper each keyword while saying the verse. Repeat 3-5 times.

Write the VERSE . . . .

and WRITE it again . . . .

Go tell SOMEONE

WHO can I tell this week?

_____

WHEN & WHERE will it happen?

_____

WHAT do I want to say?

_____

_____

WHY do I want to tell them?

_____

_____

HOW did THE PERSON receive it?

_____

_____

WHO else can I share this VERSE with?

_____

Spread the GOOD NEWS everyday . . .

Write the VERSE . . . .

_____
_____
_____
_____
_____
_____
_____
_____

and WRITE it again . . . .

_____
_____
_____
_____
_____
_____
_____
_____

Last chance to PONDER
. . . write, doodle, draw . . .

[}

Now CLOSE the journal.
& QUIZ yourself . . .
no peeking!

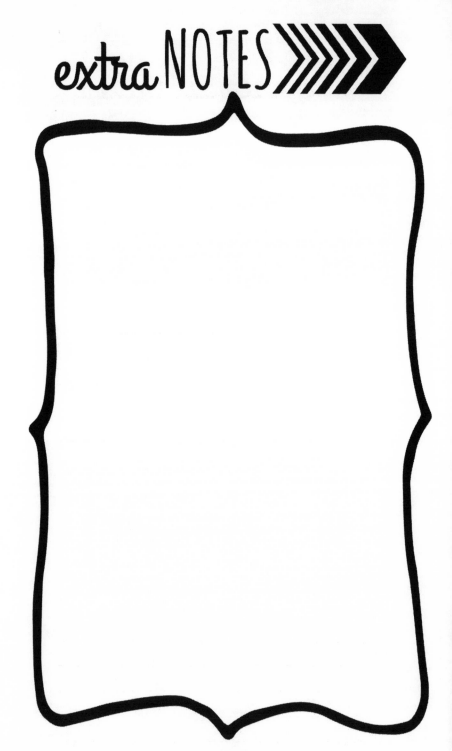

extra NOTES

My VERSE this week:

DATE:

_____
_____
_____
_____
_____
_____
_____
_____
_____
_____

What it MEANS to me . . . .

_____
_____
_____
_____
_____
_____
_____
_____
_____
_____
_____

Write the VERSE . . . .

_____

_____

_____

_____

_____

_____

and WRITE it again . . . .

_____

_____

_____

_____

_____

_____

Say it OUT loud

⬭ DAY #1
⬭ DAY #2
⬭ DAY #3
⬭ DAY #4
⬭ DAY #5
⬭ DAY #6

Draw & doodle it . . . .

Write the VERSE . . . .

_____

_____

_____

_____

_____

_____

_____

and WRITE it again . . . .

_____

_____

_____

_____

_____

_____

_____

Reflect & turn it into a PRAYER . . .

Now SAY the verse out loud.
& READ the prayer out loud.

Write the VERSE . . . .

_____

_____

_____

_____

_____

_____

_____

and WRITE it again . . . .

_____

_____

_____

_____

_____

_____

_____

_____

Pick 3 KEYWORDS
to spell & define below:

1) _____

_____

_____

_____

2) _____

_____

_____

_____

3) _____

_____

_____

_____

Now whisper each keyword while saying the verse. Repeat 3-5 times.

Write the VERSE . . . .

_____
_____
_____
_____
_____
_____
_____

and WRITE it again . . . .

_____
_____
_____
_____
_____
_____
_____

Go tell SOMEONE

WHO can I tell this week?

_____

WHEN & WHERE will it happen?

_____

WHAT do I want to say?

_____

_____

WHY do I want to tell them?

_____

_____

HOW did THE PERSON receive it?

_____

_____

WHO else can I share this VERSE with?

_____

Spread the GOOD NEWS everyday . . .

Write the VERSE . . . .

_____
_____
_____
_____
_____
_____
_____

and WRITE it again . . . .

_____
_____
_____
_____
_____
_____
_____

Last chance to PONDER

. . . write, doodle, draw . . .

[}

Now **CLOSE** *the journal.*
& **QUIZ** *yourself . . .*
no peeking!

extra NOTES

My VERSE this week:

DATE:

_____

_____

_____

_____

_____

_____

_____

_____

_____

- - - - - - - - - - - -

What it MEANS to me . . . .

_____

_____

_____

_____

_____

_____

_____

_____

_____

_____

_____

Write the VERSE . . . .

_____
_____
_____
_____
_____
_____
_____

and WRITE it again . . . .

_____
_____
_____
_____
_____
_____
_____
_____

Say it OUT loud

◯ DAY #1
◯ DAY #2
◯ DAY #3
◯ DAY #4
◯ DAY #5
◯ DAY #6

Draw & doodle it . . . .

71

Write the VERSE . . . .

_____
_____
_____
_____
_____
_____
_____
_____

and WRITE it again . . . .

_____
_____
_____
_____
_____
_____
_____
_____

Reflect & turn it into a PRAYER . . .

Now SAY the verse out loud.
& READ the prayer out loud.

Write the VERSE . . . .

_____
_____
_____
_____
_____
_____
_____

and WRITE it again . . . .

_____
_____
_____
_____
_____
_____
_____

Pick 3 KEYWORDS
to spell & define below:

1) _____

_____

_____

_____

2) _____

_____

_____

_____

3) _____

_____

_____

_____

Now whisper each keyword while saying the verse. Repeat 3-5 times.

Write the VERSE . . . .

and WRITE it again . . . .

Go tell SOMEONE

WHO can I tell this week?

_____

WHEN & WHERE will it happen?

_____

WHAT do I want to say?

_____

_____

WHY do I want to tell them?

_____

_____

HOW did THE PERSON receive it?

_____

_____

WHO else can I share this VERSE with?

_____
Spread the GOOD NEWS everyday . . .

Write the VERSE . . . .

_____
_____
_____
_____
_____
_____
_____
_____

and WRITE it again . . . .

_____
_____
_____
_____
_____
_____
_____
_____
_____

Last chance to PONDER

. . . write, doodle, draw . . .

[}

Now CLOSE the journal.
& QUIZ yourself . . .
no peeking!

extra NOTES

My VERSE this week:

DATE:

_____

_____

_____

_____

_____

_____

_____

_____

_____

- - - - - - - -

What it MEANS to me . . .

_____

_____

_____

_____

_____

_____

_____

_____

_____

_____

Write the VERSE . . . .

_____

_____

_____

_____

_____

_____

_____

and WRITE it again . . . .

_____

_____

_____

_____

_____

_____

_____

_____

Say it OUT loud

- ◯ DAY #1
- ◯ DAY #2
- ◯ DAY #3
- ◯ DAY #4
- ◯ DAY #5
- ◯ DAY #6

Draw & doodle it . . . .

Write the VERSE . . .

_____
_____
_____
_____
_____
_____
_____

and WRITE it again . . . .

_____
_____
_____
_____
_____
_____
_____

Reflect & turn it into a PRAYER . . .

Now SAY the verse out loud.
& READ the prayer out loud.

Write the VERSE . . . .

and WRITE it again . . . .

Pick 3 KEYWORDS
to spell & define below:

1) _____

_____

_____

_____

2) _____

_____

_____

_____

3) _____

_____

_____

_____

Now whisper each keyword while saying the verse. Repeat 3-5 times.

Write the VERSE . . .

and WRITE it again . . .

Go tell SOMEONE

WHO can I tell this week?

_____

WHEN & WHERE will it happen?

_____

WHAT do I want to say?

_____

_____

WHY do I want to tell them?

_____

_____

HOW did THE PERSON receive it?

_____

_____

WHO else can I share this VERSE with?

_____

Spread the GOOD NEWS everyday . . .

Write the VERSE . . . .

and WRITE it again . . . .

Last chance to PONDER
. . . write, doodle, draw . . .

Now CLOSE the journal.
& QUIZ yourself . . .
no peeking!

extra NOTES ▶▶▶▶

My VERSE this week:

DATE:

_____

What it MEANS to me . . . .

Write the VERSE . . . .

and WRITE it again . . . .

Say it OUT loud

○ DAY #1
○ DAY #2
○ DAY #3
○ DAY #4
○ DAY #5
○ DAY #6

Draw & doodle it . . . .

Write the VERSE . . . .

_____
_____
_____
_____
_____
_____
_____

and WRITE it again . . . .

_____
_____
_____
_____
_____
_____
_____

Reflect & turn it into a PRAYER . . .

_____

_____

_____

_____

_____

_____

_____

_____

_____

Now SAY the verse out loud.
& READ the prayer out loud.

Write the VERSE . . . .

_____
_____
_____
_____
_____
_____
_____

and WRITE it again . . . .

_____
_____
_____
_____
_____
_____
_____
_____

Pick 3 KEYWORDS
to spell & define below:

1) _____

_____

_____

_____

2) _____

_____

_____

_____

3) _____

_____

_____

_____

Now whisper each keyword while saying the verse. Repeat 3-5 times.

Write the VERSE . . .

and WRITE it again . . .

Go tell SOMEONE

WHO can I tell this week?

_____

WHEN & WHERE will it happen?

_____

WHAT do I want to say?

_____

_____

WHY do I want to tell them?

_____

_____

HOW did THE PERSON receive it?

_____

_____

_____

WHO else can I share this VERSE with?

_____

Spread the GOOD NEWS everyday . . .

Write the VERSE . . . .

and WRITE it again . . . .

Last chance to PONDER

... write, doodle, draw ...

Now CLOSE the journal.
& QUIZ yourself ...
no peeking!

extra NOTES

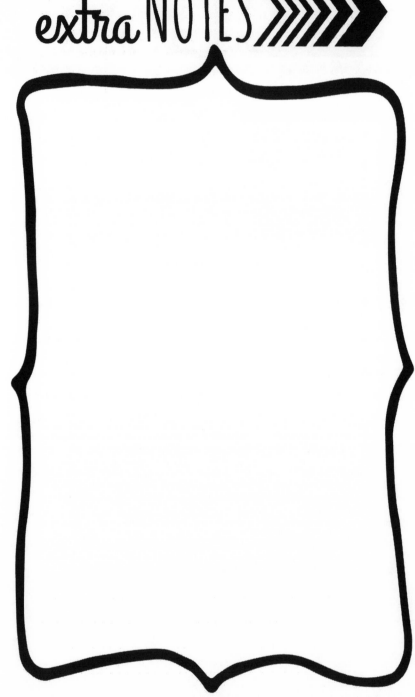

My VERSE this week:

DATE:

_____
_____
_____
_____
_____
_____
_____
_____
_____
_____

- - - - - - - - - - - -

What it MEANS to me . . .

_____
_____
_____
_____
_____
_____
_____
_____
_____
_____

Write the VERSE . . . .

and WRITE it again . . . .

Say it OUT loud

○ DAY #1
○ DAY #2
○ DAY #3
○ DAY #4
○ DAY #5
○ DAY #6

Draw & doodle it . . . .

Write the VERSE . . . .

_____
_____
_____
_____
_____
_____
_____

and WRITE it again . . . .

_____
_____
_____
_____
_____
_____
_____

Reflect & turn it into a PRAYER . . .

{ _____
_____
_____
_____
_____
_____
_____
_____
_____
_____ }

Now SAY the verse out loud.
& READ the prayer out loud.

Write the VERSE . . .

_____

_____

_____

_____

_____

_____

_____

and WRITE it again . . .

_____

_____

_____

_____

_____

_____

_____

_____

Pick 3 KEYWORDS
to spell & define below:

1) _____

_____

_____

_____

2) _____

_____

_____

_____

3) _____

_____

_____

_____

Now whisper each keyword while saying the verse. Repeat 3-5 times.

Write the VERSE....

_____

_____

_____

_____

_____

_____

_____

and WRITE it again ....

_____

_____

_____

_____

_____

_____

_____

_____

_____

Go tell SOMEONE

WHO can I tell this week?

_____

WHEN & WHERE will it happen?

_____

WHAT do I want to say?

_____

_____

_____

WHY do I want to tell them?

_____

_____

_____

HOW did THE PERSON receive it?

_____

_____

_____

WHO else can I share this VERSE with?

_____

Spread the GOOD NEWS everyday . . .

Write the VERSE . . . .

_____
_____
_____
_____
_____
_____
_____
_____

and WRITE it again . . . .

_____
_____
_____
_____
_____
_____
_____
_____
_____

Last chance to PONDER

. . . write, doodle, draw . . .

[

}

Now CLOSE the journal.
& QUIZ yourself . . .
no peeking!

extra NOTES

My VERSE this week:

DATE:

_____

_____

_____

_____

_____

_____

_____

_____

_____

_____

- - - - - - - - - -

What it MEANS to me . . .

_____

_____

_____

_____

_____

_____

_____

_____

_____

_____

_____

Write the VERSE . . . .

and WRITE it again . . .

Say it OUT loud

○ DAY #1
○ DAY #2
○ DAY #3
○ DAY #4
○ DAY #5
○ DAY #6

Draw & doodle it . . . .

Write the VERSE . . . .

and WRITE it again . . . .

Reflect & turn it into a PRAYER . . . .

Now SAY the verse out loud.
& READ the prayer out loud.

Write the VERSE . . . .

_____
_____
_____
_____
_____
_____
_____

and WRITE it again . . . .

_____
_____
_____
_____
_____
_____
_____

Pick 3 KEYWORDS
to spell & define below:

1) _____

_____

_____

_____

2) _____

_____

_____

_____

3) _____

_____

_____

_____

Now whisper each keyword while saying the verse. Repeat 3-5 times.

Write the VERSE . . . .

_____
_____
_____
_____
_____
_____
_____

and WRITE it again . . . .

_____
_____
_____
_____
_____
_____
_____

Go tell SOMEONE

WHO can I tell this week?

_____

WHEN & WHERE will it happen?

_____

WHAT do I want to say?

_____

_____

_____

WHY do I want to tell them?

_____

_____

_____

HOW did THE PERSON receive it?

_____

_____

_____

WHO else can I share this VERSE with?

_____

Spread the GOOD NEWS everyday . . .

Write the VERSE. . . .

and WRITE it again . . . .

Last chance to PONDER

. . . write, doodle, draw . . .

[}

Now CLOSE the journal.
& QUIZ yourself . . .
no peeking!

extra NOTES

My VERSE this week:

DATE:

_____
_____
_____
_____
_____
_____
_____
_____
_____

- - - - - - - - - - - -

What it MEANS to me . . . .

_____
_____
_____
_____
_____
_____
_____
_____
_____
_____

Write the VERSE....

_____

_____

_____

_____

_____

_____

and WRITE it again ....

_____

_____

_____

_____

_____

_____

_____

Say it OUT loud

○ DAY #1
○ DAY #2
○ DAY #3
○ DAY #4
○ DAY #5
○ DAY #6

Draw & doodle it . . . .

Write the VERSE . . .

_____
_____
_____
_____
_____
_____
_____

and WRITE it again . . . .

_____
_____
_____
_____
_____
_____
_____

Reflect & turn it into a PRAYER . . .

Now SAY the verse out loud.
& READ the prayer out loud.

Write the VERSE . . . .

_____

_____

_____

_____

_____

_____

_____

and WRITE it again . . . .

_____

_____

_____

_____

_____

_____

_____

_____

Pick 3 KEYWORDS
to spell & define below:

1) _____

_____

_____

_____

2) _____

_____

_____

_____

3) _____

_____

_____

_____

Now whisper each keyword while saying the verse. Repeat 3-5 times.

Write the VERSE . . . .

and WRITE it again . . . .

Go tell SOMEONE

WHO can I tell this week?

_____

WHEN & WHERE will it happen?

_____

WHAT do I want to say?

_____

_____

_____

WHY do I want to tell them?

_____

_____

_____

HOW did THE PERSON receive it?

_____

_____

_____

WHO else can I share this VERSE with?

_____

Spread the GOOD NEWS everyday . . .

137

Write the VERSE . . . .

_____

_____

_____

_____

_____

_____

_____

and WRITE it again . . . .

_____

_____

_____

_____

_____

_____

_____

_____

Last chance to PONDER

. . . write, doodle, draw . . .

Now CLOSE the journal.
& QUIZ yourself . . .
no peeking!

extra NOTES

My VERSE this week:

DATE:

_____
_____
_____
_____

_____
_____
_____
_____
_____

- - - - - - - - - - - - - - - -

What it MEANS to me . . . .

_____
_____
_____
_____
_____
_____
_____
_____
_____
_____

Write the VERSE . . . .

and WRITE it again . . . .

Say it OUT loud

○ DAY #1
○ DAY #2
○ DAY #3
○ DAY #4
○ DAY #5
○ DAY #6

Draw & doodle it . . . .

Write the VERSE . . . .

_____
_____
_____
_____
_____
_____
_____

and WRITE it again . . . .

_____
_____
_____
_____
_____
_____
_____

Reflect & turn it into a PRAYER . . .

Now SAY the verse out loud.
& READ the prayer out loud.

Write the VERSE . . . .

_____

_____

_____

_____

_____

_____

_____

and WRITE it again . . . .

_____

_____

_____

_____

_____

_____

_____

_____

Pick 3 KEYWORDS
to spell & define below:

1) _____

_____

_____

_____

2) _____

_____

_____

_____

3) _____

_____

_____

_____

Now whisper each keyword while saying the verse. Repeat 3-5 times.

Write the VERSE . . .

_____

_____

_____

_____

_____

_____

_____

and WRITE it again . . .

_____

_____

_____

_____

_____

_____

_____

Go tell SOMEONE

WHO can I tell this week?

_____

WHEN & WHERE will it happen?

_____

WHAT do I want to say?

_____
_____

WHY do I want to tell them?

_____
_____

HOW did THE PERSON receive it?

_____
_____

WHO else can I share this VERSE with?

_____

Spread the GOOD NEWS everyday . . .

Write the VERSE. . . .

_____

_____

_____

_____

_____

_____

and WRITE it again . . .

_____

_____

_____

_____

_____

_____

_____

Last chance to PONDER

. . . write, doodle, draw . . .

[}

Now CLOSE the journal.
& QUIZ yourself . . .
no peeking!

extra NOTES ►►►►

Do you REMEMBER?

List each verse & give yourself an oral quiz.

☐ 1) _____

☐ 2) _____

☐ 3) _____

☐ 4) _____

☐ 5) _____

☐ 6) _____

☐ 7) _____

☐ 8) _____

☐ 9) _____

☐ 10) _____

☐ 11) _____

☐ 12) _____

⟹ Score: ☐ /12

153

CONGRATULATIONS!

. . . you did it . . .

Don't stop your BIBLE VERSE ➜ memory journey now . . . Keep on WRITING it, doodling it, SAYING it, pondering it, & PRAYING it so that YOU hide God's word in your HEART  (Psalm 119:11).

Thank you for using one of our journals!

Our family appreciates your purchase and
feedback. If you found this journal useful
(hopefully a bit life-changing too), we ask
you to tell a friend and consider writing
a review. Our goal is to spread the good
news of Jesus and inspire others to learn
more about God's word...one journal at a time.

With much ♥,
The Frisby's
Stephen, Shalana & Rowynn

p.s. Check out our website for other fun journals!

1.2.3...journal it!

find more about us at www.123journalit.com
... self-guided DIY study books for the whole family ...

If you like this journal, please share it
and spread the word! #123journalit